connections

Linking Manipulatives to Mathematics ✦ Grade 2

Linda Holden Charles
Micaelia Randolph Brummett

Creative Publications

Cover design by JoAnne Hammer

Illustrated by Jeani Brunnick
Elaine Abe

© 1989 Creative Publications
788 Palomar Avenue
Sunnyvale, California 94086
Printed in U.S.A.

ISBN: 0-88488-769-3

1 2 3 4 5 6 7 8 9 10. 9 5 4 3 2 1 0 8 9

Table of Contents

Money

Geometric Thinking

Fractions

Multiplication

Lesson Resources

Notes to the Teacher

What is *Connections*?

Connections is a series of six resource books for grades one through six. Each resource book offers twenty classic manipulative lessons carefully designed to teach the most important math topics of that grade.

Combined with the Connections Manipulative Kits for each grade, these resource books provide a unique program that integrates quality manipulative teaching into any existing math curriculum.

What is the philosophy of *Connections*?

Connections is based on the knowledge that active learning is the foundation for understanding. Each lesson is designed to develop concepts by connecting:

- student experiences with materials
- language
- mathematics

The key elements of each lesson ensure this connection:

- exploring with manipulatives
- recording
- reporting and displaying

Why should I teach with *Connections*?

Connections solves all the problems of teaching with manipulatives. The twenty most important lessons for your grade have been selected for you. Lessons are structured to work with a whole class of children. The best grouping plan for each lesson is listed and the exact quantities of materials needed for those groups are given. The blackline student recording sheets for each lesson are included in your *Connections* resource book. If you are using the Connections Manipulative Kit for your grade, you will only need to add classroom supplies (crayons, scissors, colored paper, etc.) to have all the materials needed for the twenty lessons.

How is *Connections* organized?

Inside your *Connections* resource book are 20 four-page lessons. The lessons are organized in a curricular sequence similar to the math textbook you are using. Look at the topics in the Table of Contents and weave the *Connections* lessons into your math outline for the school year.

What is a typical lesson like?

Each page in a *Connections* lesson has a special function to help you present the activity to your children.

The first page tells you the title, the manipulative, and the math topic. You are given a short description of the lesson and a drawing of children involved in the activity. The best grouping plan for your children is outlined, and you are given an exact materials list for each group.

The second page is a complete set of directions for the lesson. You are given an idea for introducing the lesson, a step-by-step plan for exploring the concept using the manipulative, and complete suggestions for recording student findings.

The third page discusses ways to involve children in reporting, discussing, and organizing their findings. A typical classroom display of student work is shown along with solutions when appropriate.

The fourth page is a blackline master of the student recording sheet for the activity.

How should I organize my children?

Connections outlines several different class grouping plans. These three are the most common:

- Eight groups of four, sharing materials, working together
- Eight groups of four, sharing materials, working independently
- Eight groups of four, sharing materials, working in pairs

Sometimes six groups of five, or five groups of six are used. Occasionally the whole class works together.

The grouping plan is carefully chosen to work best with the activity and the materials available.

How should I organize my manipulatives?

The lessons in *Connections* are designed to work with the quantities of materials in the Connections Manipulative Kit for that grade level.

The Connections Manipulative Kit for Grade Two (Cat. No. 10948) includes the following materials:

2 buckets Unifix® Cubes
2 buckets plastic Pattern Blocks
1 bucket Plastic Coins
1 bucket Teddy Bear Counters
1 set Pattern Blocks for the overhead projector
1 set Colored Squares for the overhead projector
1 set Coins for the overhead projector
1 set Teddy Bears for the overhead projector

For most lessons, you will be organizing your class into eight groups of four. When this is the case, organize your materials as discussed below. If the organization of materials is different from this, you will be given specific directions on that lesson page.

Pattern Blocks: Put in eight containers. Each container should have 6 yellow, 6 orange, 12 red, 12 blue, 12 white, 12 green.

Unifix® Cubes: Put in eight containers. Each container should have 75 cubes.

Base Ten Blocks: Put in eight containers. Each container should have 37 units, 18 rods, and 1 flat.

Teddy Bear Counters: Put in eight containers. Each container should have 37 bears.

Plastic Coins: There are eight sets. Each set contains 30 pennies, 24 nickels, 20 dimes, 16 quarters, and 4 half-dollars.

What about the lesson resource pages?

In *Connections*: Grade Two, there are nine pages at the back of the book that are used in various ways with some of the lessons. Following are suggestions for preparing these pages. If blocks, bears, and coins are cut apart before the lesson begins, the children will have more time for the activity. In this case, you may be able to eliminate scissors from the lesson materials list.

Page 84: Unifix® Paper

Duplicate on white paper. Distribute whole sheets. Children will color squares to match Unifix Cubes and cut apart into strips.

Page 85: Centimeter Grid Paper

Duplicate on white paper. Distribute whole sheets. Children will color squares and cut apart into strips.

Pages 86-90: Paper Pattern Blocks

Duplicate each page on the color paper that matches that particular block. Cut apart and put into low containers (butter tubs, for example) before beginning the activity. Many teachers let children cut the pieces apart at a "scissors center" on a day prior to the lesson.

Page 91: Paper Teddy Bears

Duplicate on white paper and let children color during the activity or duplicate on colored paper to match the colors of the bears (red, blue, yellow, green). Cut apart (the paper cutter is fastest) and put into low containers before beginning the activity. If the lesson calls for stand-up bears, cut apart so tab is left on. If not, cut tab off.

Page 92: Paper Coins

Duplicate on white paper. Cut apart and put into low containers before beginning the activity.

Castle Walls

In this lesson, children stand Pattern Blocks up on edge to form long pattern walls. They arrange the blocks in a continuing linear pattern and record by pasting paper blocks. Use this lesson to teach children to create and extend patterns.

Classroom Organization

Eight groups of four sharing materials
Working independently

Materials

Each group of four children will need these materials:
• Pattern Blocks, see page 3 • 4 copies of Castle Wall Recording Sheet, page 7 • Adding machine tape (about 24" for each child) • Paper Pattern Blocks, pages 86-90 • Paste and crayons

4

Introducing the Problem

All the kings and queens have decided they would like to have brightly colored Pattern Blocks walls around their castles. Each pattern must be interesting and the pattern must repeat over and over again.

Can you make a Pattern Blocks wall for one of the castles?

Exploring with Pattern Blocks

1. Have the children choose Pattern Blocks and make a wall with a repeating pattern.

2. Encourage the children to talk about the different walls that they make. Have them read their patterns, saying the names of the shapes or the colors (triangle, triangle, square, triangle, triangle, square...).

Recording the Connection

1. Tell children their task is to copy their pattern onto adding machine tape *walls* with paper Pattern Blocks. Tell them to repeat the pattern over and over until the wall is completed.

2. When children finish their walls, they should tape the ends together to form circles and stand them up like real walls.

3. Children should cut out the castle on the Castle Walls Recording Sheet, roll it into a cylinder and paste so it will stand up. Children may also draw, color, and cut out their own stand-up castles. Have children place their castles inside their walls.

Reporting and Displaying

When all the castles and castle walls are completed, bring the class together for a look at what they have done. Examine the different walls and discuss how they are alike and different. Investigate various ways of displaying the castles and walls on a table or a clear space on the floor. Sort them into groups many different ways.

Castle Walls

Suggestions

Children will probably make many different patterns for the castle wall. It is important to give them an opportunity to describe the various patterns they make. The class display is a perfect opportunity to practice sorting and classifying skills as children look for likenesses and differences among the walls and castles. Don't overlook the chance to develop math language.

For more activity ideas, see *Primary Jobcards™: Patterns With Pattern Blocks*, Creative Publications, Catalog Number 34523.

Castle Walls

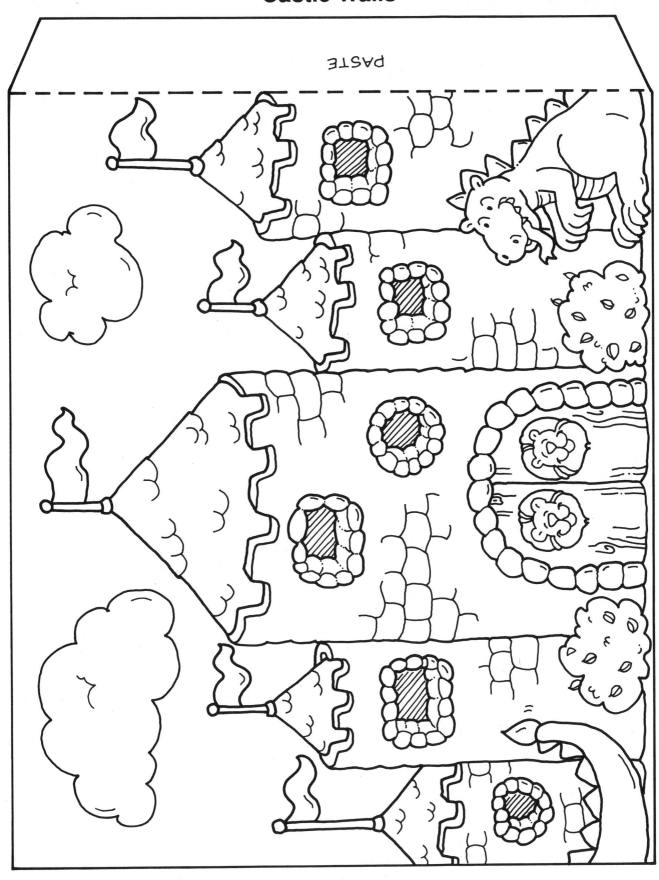

PASTE

CONNECTIONS: GRADE 2
Castle Walls Recording Sheet

Train Wreck

In this lesson, children investigate long Unifix train patterns and the patterns that are made by breaking them apart in a regular way to form a design. Use this lesson to reinforce number and pattern concepts and to extend classification and discussion skills.

Classroom Organization

Fifteen groups of two
Working in pairs

Materials

Each pair of children will need these materials:
• Unifix® Cubes (4 ten-cube sticks, 2 each of 2 colors, 40 cubes altogether) • 4 copies of Unifix® Paper, page 84 • 1 copy of Train Wreck Recording Sheet, page 11 • Scissors, crayons, and paste

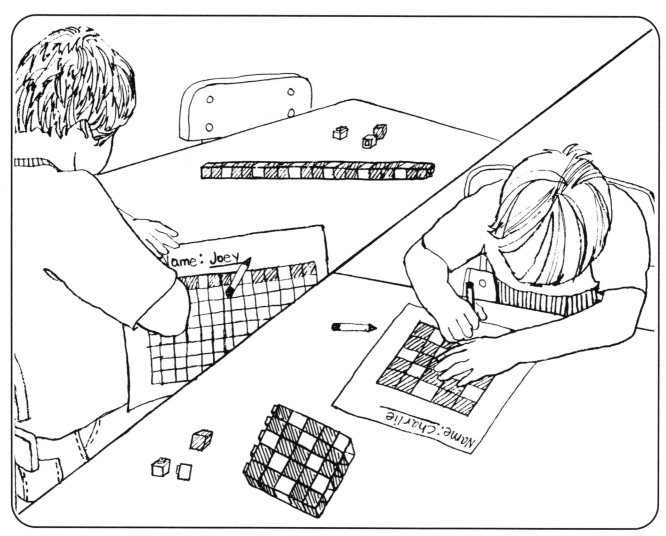

CONNECTIONS: GRADE 2
© 1989 Creative Publications

Introducing the Problem

Today we are going to make pattern trains out of Unifix Cubes. You are going to listen to some patterns we make with our hands and our feet and make the same pattern with your cubes.

What do you think your pattern will look like?

Exploring with Unifix® Cubes

1. Start this pattern and tell the children to join in—clap, clap, pat your lap, clap, clap, pat, and so on.

2. Tell the children to make a pattern with their cubes that is the same as the clap, clap, pat pattern (for example, red, red, blue). Notice that each group will use different colors but the pattern structures will be the same.

3. Repeat several times with different patterns.

4. Have all the children make a cube pattern from a simple pattern such as snap, clap, snap, clap.

5. Tell the children that the pattern trains jump the track and have a wreck! But they wreck in a very special way. They break apart into pieces with the same number of cars in each piece. Show the children how to break their trains into twos and stack up the pieces.

6. Have the children put their trains back together retaining the original pattern. Each pair should break their train apart again. They should break the train into one of these: threes, fours, fives, or sixes, and stack them as they did in the example above.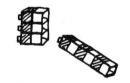

7. Look at the different patterns created and discuss. Who got stripes? Who got diagonals?

Recording the Connection

1. Have the children make new patterns with their cubes. Check the patterns as children complete them. Tell them to color the squares at the tops of the recording sheets to show their patterns.

2. Next, children should break their patterns into threes and color Unifix paper to record. They should cut out the 3-train from their recording sheet and paste it onto their pattern.

3. Put the patterns back together and repeat for fours, fives, and sixes.

Reporting and Displaying

Each group will have five pieces of paper to display: The strip with the record of their pattern, and four pieces of Unifix paper showing the design made by breaking the train into threes, fours, fives, and sixes. These can be pasted onto large pieces of paper for each pair or displayed on a large bulletin board.

As the groups display their work, look for patterns that are the same in structure but different in color. Their break-apart designs should also be the same.

Solutions and Suggestions

Look for patterns that are different but produce similar designs. Talk about what kinds of patterns produce stripes, diagonals, and checkerboards, when they break apart in certain ways. This activity is rich with classification possiblities.

For more activity ideas, see *Hands On Unifix® Cubes*, Creative Publications, Catalog Number 30279.

CONNECTIONS: GRADE 2
© 1989 Creative Publications

Train Wreck

Names _____   _____

Our pattern is:

3-Train

PASTE

4-Train

PASTE

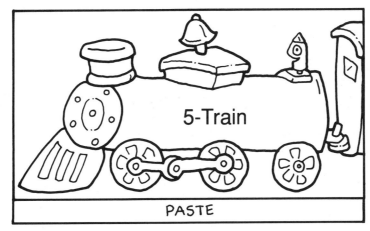

5-Train

PASTE

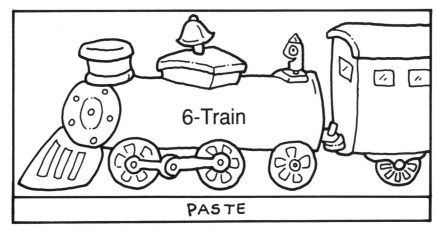

6-Train

PASTE

CONNECTIONS: GRADE 2
Train Wreck Recording Sheet
© 1989 Creative Publications

Teddy Bear Marching Band

In this lesson, children line up Teddy Bear Counters in twos, threes, fours, and fives. They practice skip counting aloud and make the abstract connection by writing the skip counting numbers. Use this lesson early in the year to reinforce number patterns and repeat later in the year as readiness for multiplication.

Classroom Organization

Eight groups of four sharing materials
Working together

Materials

Each group of four children will need these materials:
• 37 Teddy Bear Counters • 4 copies of Teddy Bear Marching Band Recording Sheet, page 15 • 8 copies of Paper Teddy Bears, page 91 • 1 large piece of construction or butcher paper • Crayons, paste, and scissors

CONNECTIONS: GRADE 2
© 1989 Creative Publications

Introducing the Problem

The teddy bears are getting ready to march in the band. Sometimes they march by twos, sometimes by threes, sometimes by fours, and sometimes by fives.

Let's count them as they line up for the parade.

Exploring with Teddy Bear Counters

1. Have the children work together to arrange all 36 bears into a line marching two by two. Count the bears by twos aloud together.

2. Rearrange the bears into a line marching three by three. Count the bears by threes aloud together.

3. Repeat with the bears marching by fours, then fives.

Recording the Connection

1. Have children cut out and color stand-up bears and paste them into marching bands on the butcher paper. Each group should have a two-by-two band, a three-by-three band, a four-by-four band, and a five-by-five band.

2. They should cut out the drum majors from the recording sheets and paste them in front of each band.

3. Have the children write the skip-counting numbers next to each row of bears.

Reporting and Displaying

Display each groups' parade of bears on a table or counter top where they can see one another's work.

Give the children lots of practice skip counting out loud as you admire the different parades.

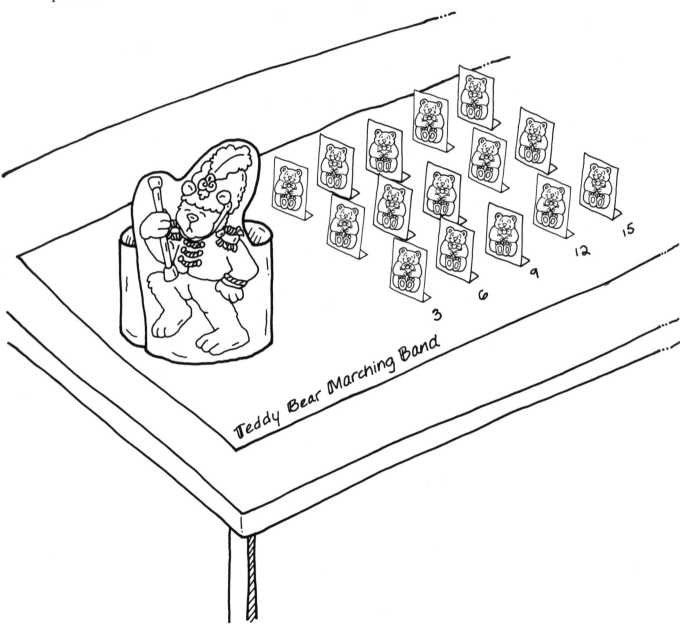

Teddy Bear Marching Band

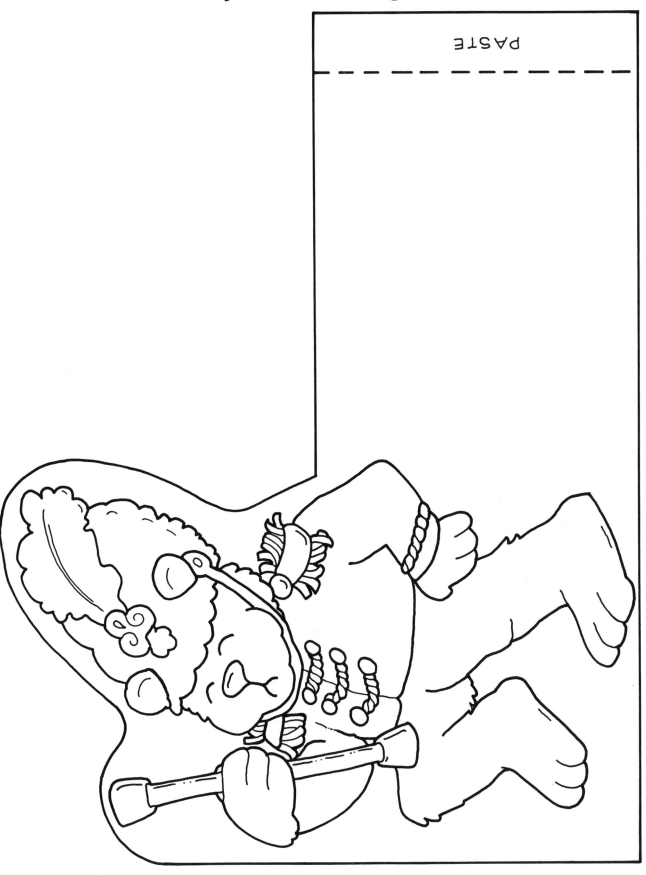

PASTE

CONNECTIONS: GRADE 2
Teddy Bear Marching Band Recording Sheet

Pattern Blocks Facts

In this lesson, children arrange two colors of Pattern Blocks to make a design and write an addition equation to describe the numbers of blocks in the design. Use this lesson to develop the concept of addition.

Classroom Organization

Eight groups of four sharing materials
Working independently

Materials

Each group of four children will need these materials:
• Pattern Blocks, see page 3 • 20 copies of Pattern Blocks Facts Recording Sheet, page 19
• Paper Pattern Blocks, pages 86-90 • Scissors and paste

CONNECTIONS: GRADE 2
© 1989 Creative Publications

Introducing the Problem

You are going to make designs or pictures with two colors of Pattern Blocks and write addition equations to go with them.

How many different equations do you think you can write?

Exploring with Pattern Blocks

1. Tell the children to take two colors of Pattern Blocks and make a design or picture.

2. Have the children practice saying an additon equation that tells about the numbers of blocks in their design. For example, four reds and five blues would be $4 + 5 = 9$.

Recording the Connection

1. The children should paste paper Pattern Blocks on their recording sheet to match the design.

2. Tell them to write an addition equation that tells about the design. For example, seven reds and eight blues would be $7 + 8 = 15$.

3. Children should repeat, making several Pattern Blocks facts.

Reporting and Displaying

When each child has had a chance to record several Pattern Blocks facts, collect and display them on a wall where everyone can see them. Ask children for suggestions about how to put the pictures together into groups that are alike in some way. Arrange and display the facts to match one of the suggestions.

Over the next several days, children may continue to add to the facts collection. Rearrange the facts display into different groups using new ways to classify.

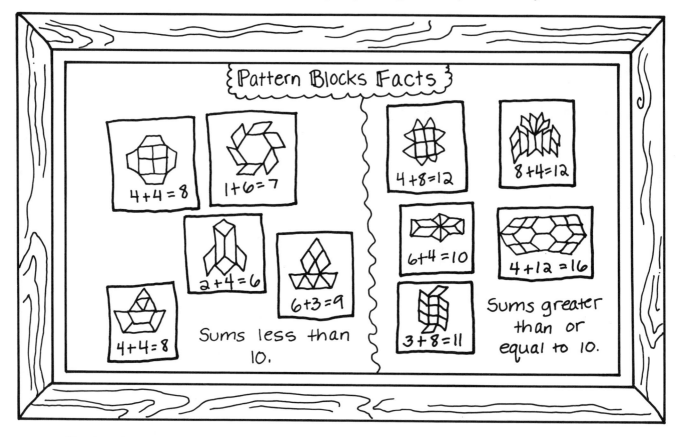

Solutions and Suggestions

Children will write many different equations, with many different designs. Encourage them to think of different ways to put the facts into groups (facts exactly alike, sums alike, facts with 7s in them, facts that use red blocks, etc.).

For more activity ideas, see *Story Problems With Pattern Blocks*, Creative Publications, Catalog Number 34494.

Pattern Blocks Facts

Name _____

This Pattern Blocks Picture shows _____.

CONNECTIONS: GRADE 2
Pattern Blocks Facts Recording Sheet
© 1989 Creative Publications

19

Addition Facts 100

In this lesson, children work with Unifix Cubes to build all the basic facts in the addition facts chart. This is a good culminating activity to use after some weeks of work on basic facts.

Classroom Organization

Eight groups of four sharing materials
Working independently

Materials

Each group of four children will need these materials:
• 75 Unifix® Cubes • 10 copies of Addition Facts 100 Recording Sheet, page 23
• 4 copies of Centimeter Grid Paper, page 85 • Crayons, scissors, and paste

CONNECTIONS: GRADE 2
© 1989 Creative Publications

Introducing the Problem

You are going to think of addition facts and then show them with two colors of cubes. We're going to try to think of all the addition facts we can.

Everybody make five facts and then we'll see what we have.

Exploring with Unifix® Cubes

1. Have children work independently at their tables and make addition fact sticks with two colors of cubes.

2. After everyone has had a chance to make several sticks, let different children report on the facts they made. They should hold up their sticks and tell the addition facts they represent. For example, a stick with four red cubes and five blue cubes tells the addition fact 4 + 5 = 9.

3. See how many other children chose to make the same fact.

Recording the Connection

1. Show children how to record their work by cutting out a strip of grid paper for each fact they made and coloring it to match their Unifix Cubes.

2. They should paste the paper strip onto their recording sheet and then write the addition fact underneath it.

Reporting and Displaying

When children have finished their recording sheets, tell them you want to display their work on an addition facts board. Have them begin telling the facts they have made and start putting them up. When more than one person makes the same fact, put the sheets on top of each other.

Keep working until all the sheets are on the board. Discuss which facts were made most often. Note which facts are not represented at all. Challenge children to make examples of facts that are missing.

Your class may want to work on this board over a period of several days until there is a recording sheet for each of the basic facts. A center for this purpose could be set up with recording sheets, cubes, graph paper, and crayons. When complete, the chart can serve as a permanent display for review and reference.

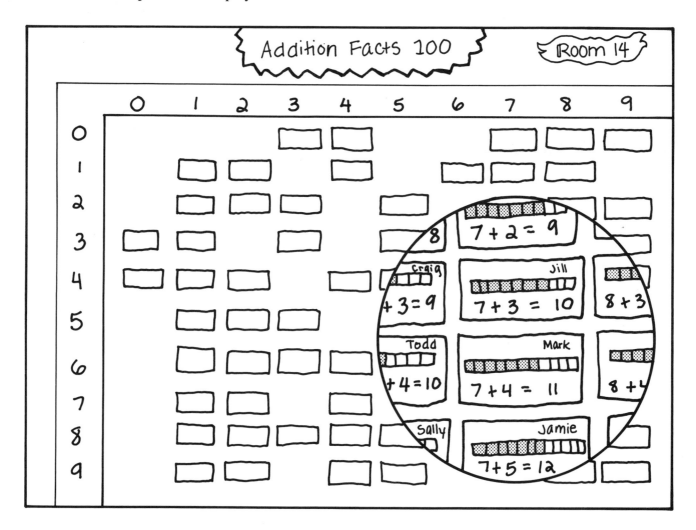

22

Addition Facts 100   Name _____

_____

- -

Addition Facts 100   Name _____

_____

CONNECTIONS: GRADE 2
Addition Facts 100 Recording Sheet
© 1989 Creative Publications

Bears in Trees

In this lesson, children make up story problems of their own that tell about pictures they create with teddy bears. This problem formulation process extends children's understanding of addition and subtraction. Use this lesson to enrich work with basic facts.

Classroom Organization

Eight groups of four sharing materials
Working independently

Materials

Each group of four children will need these materials:
• 37 Teddy Bear Counters • 4 copies of Bears in Trees Recording Sheet, page 27 • 4 copies of Paper Teddy Bears, page 91 • 4 sheets of blank writing paper • Crayons, scissors, and paste

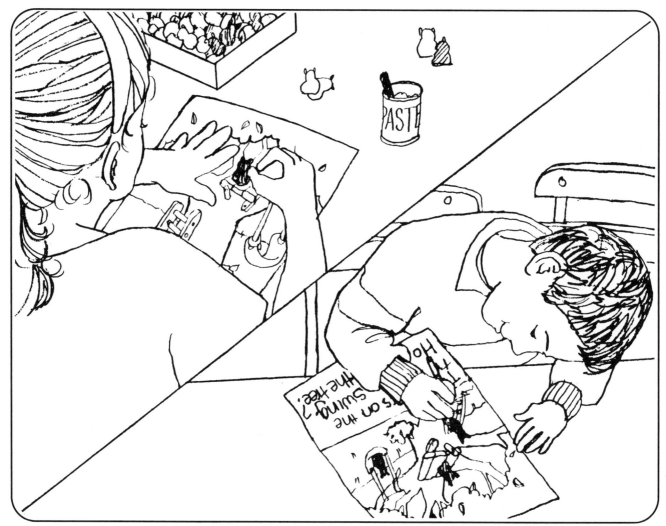

CONNECTIONS: GRADE 2
© 1989 Creative Publications

Introducing the Problem

One of the little bears in the neighborhood has a wonderful big tree in the backyard! The rest of the bears love to go over and play in the tree.

What are some of the things the bears might do when they play in the tree?

Exploring with Teddy Bear Counters

1. Have children look at the picture on their recording sheets. Discuss some of the things the little bears might do in the tree.

2. Tell them to put some Teddy Bear Counters in different locations on the tree. Then ask someone to tell a story about his or her picture.

3. After several children have had a chance to tell stories, ask someone to make up a math story about the bears and the tree: **Two bears are on the swing. Four bears are in the treehouse. How many bears are playing altogether?** Or, **Six bears were climbing the tree. Three climbed down to eat lunch. How many bears are still in the tree?**

4. Give children many chances to make up and tell story problems on their own. Depending upon the ability of the group, stories will probably range from simple statements containing numbers to story problems that end with a question.

Recording the Connection

1. Children can make a permanent record of their work by coloring paper bears and pasting them on their tree pictures.

2. They should write their story problems on separate pieces of paper and attach them to their pictures.

3. Encourage the children to include a *how many* question with their story problems.

Reporting and Displaying

When everyone has made a story problem, they can be bound together in a large class book. The problems can serve as the basis for an independent math center. Children could go to the center, choose problems from the book, and solve them with Teddy Bear Counters. They could record their work on extra copies of the Bears in Trees Recording Sheet and write their equation and solution at the bottom of the page.

Suggestions

For more activity ideas, see *Story Problems With Teddy Bear Counters*, Creative Publications, Catalog Number 30888.

Bears in Trees

Name _____

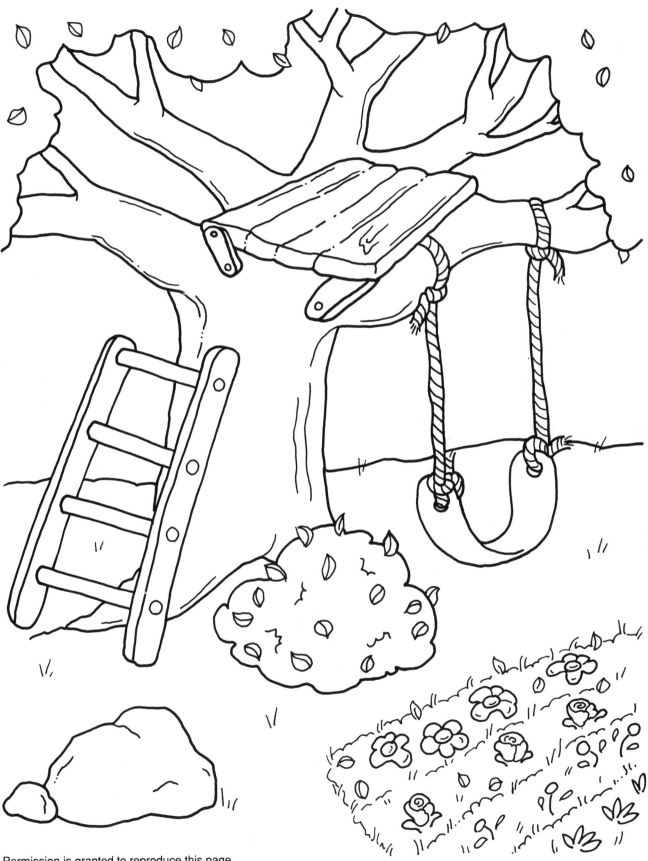

CONNECTIONS: GRADE 2
Bears in Trees Recording Sheet

Bears in Wagons

In this lesson, children try to figure out all the different ways to distribute ten bears in different numbers of wagons. It is an excellent problem-solving activity, and can be used any time children can count to ten and add successfully with more than two addends.

Classroom Organization

Eight groups of four sharing materials
Working in pairs

Materials

Each group of four children will need these materials:
• 37 Teddy Bear Counters • 6 copies of Bears in Wagons Recording Sheet, page 31 • 3 copies of Paper Teddy Bears, page 91 • 4 pieces of 12 x 18 inch construction or butcher paper • Crayons, scissors, and paste

CONNECTIONS: GRADE 2
© 1989 Creative Publications

Introducing the Problem

Ten little bears are going on a trip to the fair. They are getting ready to pile into wagons. They can take as many wagons as they want, but there must always be at least one bear in a wagon.

How many different ways can they ride to the fair?

Exploring with Teddy Bear Counters

1. Try one together. Tell the children to suppose the bears want to take four wagons. Ask them to put the ten bears in four wagons.

2. Have the children work in pairs. Let them distribute the ten bears into four groups. Discuss the different ways they discover, then talk about the different addition equations the pictures suggest.

3. Let children work together on their own with other numbers of wagons.

Recording the Connection

1. Children should record their work by pasting wagons on sheets of paper and then pasting paper bears in the wagons.

2. They should write the addition equations that tell about their pictures.

3. Encourage them to do several pictures.

Reporting and Displaying

When children have finished their pictures, display them by sorting the pictures according to the number of wagons shown.

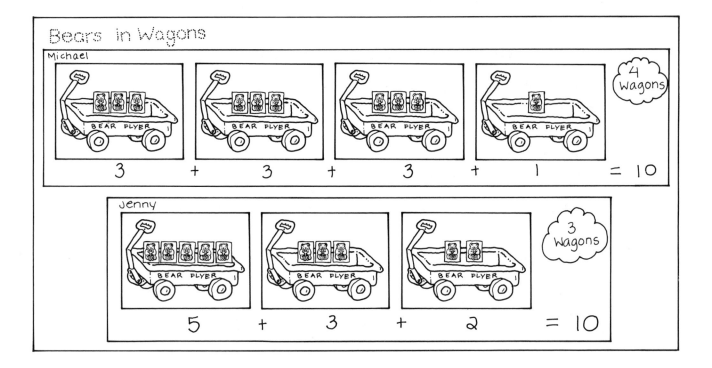

Solutions and Suggestions

There are many solutions to this problem. Children are not likely to discover them all, and they are unlikely to solve the problem in a systematic way, but they will find it interesting to look for the ways.

10 wagons — 1 way	5 wagons — 7 ways
9 wagons — 1 way	4 wagons — 9 ways
8 wagons — 2 ways	3 wagons — 8 ways
7 wagons — 3 ways	2 wagons — 5 ways
6 wagons — 5 ways	1 wagon — 1 way

CONNECTIONS: GRADE 2
© 1989 Creative Publications

Bears in Wagons

Name _____

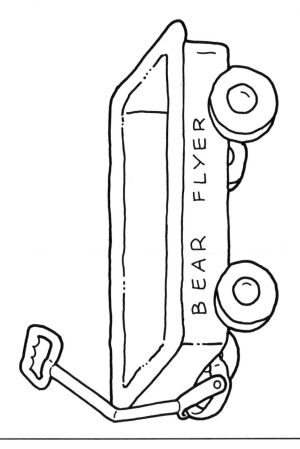 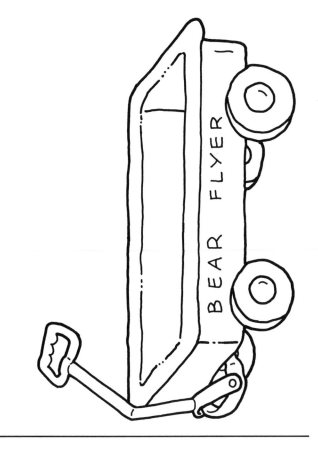

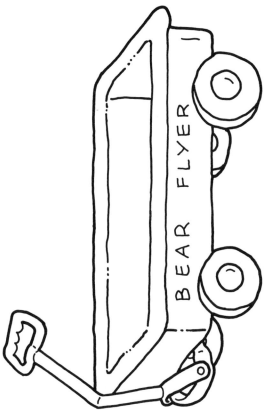 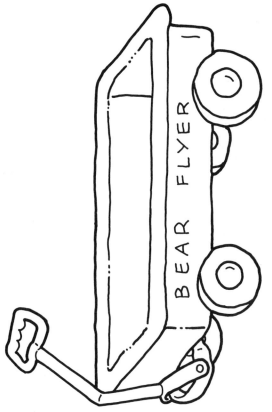

CONNECTIONS: GRADE 2
Bears in Wagons Recording Sheet

 **Teddy Bear Counters**

Missing Addends

Bears in Backpacks

In this lesson, children work with their Teddy Bear Counters to build addition equations and then use a fanciful situation to make one of the addends in each equation *go away*. They make the missing addend reappear later. Use this lesson after children have developed some skill with basic addition and subtraction facts and before they have done addition and subtraction with two-digit numbers.

Classroom Organization

Eight groups of four sharing materials
Working in pairs

Materials

Each group of four children will need these materials:
• 37 Teddy Bear Counters • 4 copies of Bears in Backpacks Recording Sheet, page 35 •
2 sheets of self-adhesive dots

32

CONNECTIONS: GRADE 2
© 1989 Creative Publications

Introducing the Problem

The little bears are on a camping trip and they've decided to go on hikes today. They can choose from the Wildflower Hike, the River Hike, the Birdwatching Hike, the Hilltop Hike, or the Pinecone Hike. Mr. Bear needs to know who wants to go where.

Can you help him make his list?

Exploring with Teddy Bear Counters

1. Work on Mr. Bear's list together. Tell the children to suppose that five red bears and three yellow bears want to go on one of the hikes.

2. Have them use their teddy bears to show what that would look like.

3. Ask them to tell you the addition equation you should write down. Write $5 + 3 = 8$ on the chalkboard.

4. Repeat the same procedure with several other equations.

5. Erase one addend in each equation and tell the children that while Mr. Bear was walking along, he dropped his list in a puddle and smeared some of his numbers!

6. Tell the children to help Mr. Bear figure out what the missing numbers are. Let them tell the missing addends and explain how they figured them out, either by using their counters, by counting up or back, or by recalling facts.

Recording the Connection

1. Let children use their recording sheets to work on their own lists for Mr. Bear.

2. When they are through, they should trade papers with a friend. The friend should make one of the numbers disappear from each equation by covering it with a self-adhesive dot.

3. Then they should return the papers to the original owners. Let everyone try to figure out the missing numbers on his or her paper. They may use teddy bears to show the story again; they may use a counting strategy; or they may recall a basic fact.

Reporting and Displaying

When all the children have completed their lists for Mr. Bear, let them tell about some of their equations and explain how they figured out the missing addends.

You may want to let children color their recording sheets and then display them on the bulletin board.

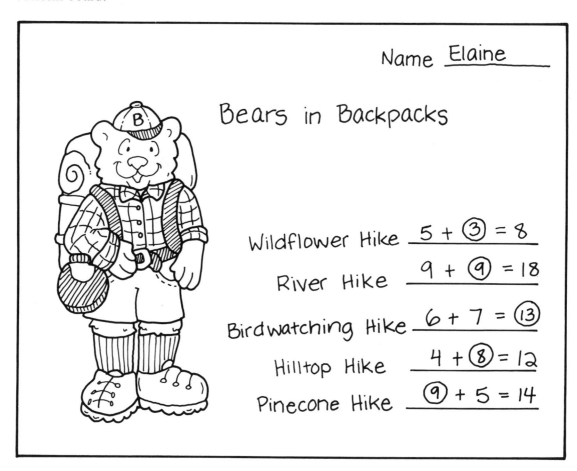

Name Elaine

Bears in Backpacks

Wildflower Hike $5 + ③ = 8$

River Hike $9 + ⑨ = 18$

Birdwatching Hike $6 + 7 = ⑬$

Hilltop Hike $4 + ⑧ = 12$

Pinecone Hike $⑨ + 5 = 14$

Suggestions

For more activity ideas, see *Understanding Operations: Addition and Subtraction*, Creative Publications, Catalog Number 31051.

CONNECTIONS: GRADE 2
© 1989 Creative Publications

Bears in Backpacks

Name _____

Wildflower Hike _____

River Hike _____

Birdwatching Hike _____

Hilltop Hike _____

Pinecone Hike _____

CONNECTIONS: GRADE 2
Bears in Backpacks Recording Sheet
© 1989 Creative Publications

Big Number Count

In this lesson, children count Unifix Cubes aloud from 1 to 600, grouping each ten together into a stick and grouping sticks into hundreds, as the teacher records the corresponding numbers. This connects each number from 1 to 600 to a physical model. Use this lesson to introduce the place value concepts of ones, tens, and hundreds.

Classroom Organization

Whole class sitting in a circle on the floor

Materials

• 600 Unifix® Cubes (20 cubes for each child) • A strip of paper divided into two columns (long enough to write the numbers 1-600) • 6 shoe box lids • 6 copies of Big Number Count Recording Sheet for each child, page 36, for lesson follow-up

CONNECTIONS: GRADE 2
© 1989 Creative Publications

Introducing the Problem

We are going to count Unifix Cubes all the way to 600 today. As you show the numbers with cubes and count them out loud, I am going to write each number on the paper strip.

How long do you think it will take us to count to 600?

Exploring with Unifix® Cubes

1. Display the long paper strip where children can see it.

2. Have the first child toss one cube into the center of the circle. Write 1 on the paper strip.

3. Continue taking turns around the circle with each child adding one cube to the pile while everyone says the number aloud. Each time, record the corresponding number on the paper strip.

4. Stop when there are ten cubes and tell the children that whenever there are ten cubes, they will put them together to make a stick. Write 10 on the paper strip and discuss the relationship between the number and the cubes. Can you see the 1 in the cubes? Can you see the 0? (1 ten-cube stick; no loose cubes)

5. Continue around the circle, adding one cube at a time, saying and recording the number. Make a ten-cube stick each time there are ten loose cubes. Make a group of 100 each time there are 10 ten-cube sticks. (This group can be made by putting the sticks into a shoe box lid.) Stop at random points and discuss the relationship between the number and the cubes.

Recording the Connection

1. Children should individually complete six Big Number Count recording sheets, starting with 101 on the second sheet, 201 on the third, etc.

2. Tell children to look for number patterns as they write the numbers.

3. Put the pages together to make a *Book of 600*. (Some children may wish to continue their books to 1000.)

Reporting and Displaying

When the children have completed their recording sheets, examine them and the long number strip together, looking for number patterns.

Solutions and Suggestions

The children will notice several patterns in the numbers. Ask them how the patterns are alike and different on the strip and on the recording sheets.

For more activity ideas, see *Understanding Place Value: Addition and Subtraction*, Creative Publications, Catalog Number 10965.

CONNECTIONS: GRADE 2
© 1989 Creative Publications

Big Number Count

Name _____

<table>
<tr><td></td><td></td><td></td><td></td><td></td><td></td><td></td><td></td><td></td><td></td></tr>
<tr><td></td><td></td><td></td><td></td><td></td><td></td><td></td><td></td><td></td><td></td></tr>
<tr><td></td><td></td><td></td><td></td><td></td><td></td><td></td><td></td><td></td><td></td></tr>
<tr><td></td><td></td><td></td><td></td><td></td><td></td><td></td><td></td><td></td><td></td></tr>
<tr><td></td><td></td><td></td><td></td><td></td><td></td><td></td><td></td><td></td><td></td></tr>
<tr><td></td><td></td><td></td><td></td><td></td><td></td><td></td><td></td><td></td><td></td></tr>
<tr><td></td><td></td><td></td><td></td><td></td><td></td><td></td><td></td><td></td><td></td></tr>
<tr><td></td><td></td><td></td><td></td><td></td><td></td><td></td><td></td><td></td><td></td></tr>
<tr><td></td><td></td><td></td><td></td><td></td><td></td><td></td><td></td><td></td><td></td></tr>
<tr><td></td><td></td><td></td><td></td><td></td><td></td><td></td><td></td><td></td><td></td></tr>
</table>

CONNECTIONS: GRADE 2
Big Number Count Recording Sheet
© 1989 Creative Publications

Hitting 100

In this lesson, children use Unifix Cubes to generate a number sequence as they add the same number of cubes over and over. They record the number after each addition, connecting the cube display to the abstract number. They also practice regrouping as they make a ten-cube stick out of ten loose cubes whenever possible. Use this lesson before teaching addition with regrouping.

Classroom Organization

Six groups of five sharing materials
Working together

Materials

Each group of five children will need these materials:
• 100 Unifix® Cubes • 3 copies of Hitting 100 Recording Sheet, page 43

Introducing the Problem

We are going to see what happens when we add the same number over and over. We are going to show the numbers with cubes as we go. We will try it with different starting numbers and different adding numbers and see how close we get to 100.

Do you think we will ever hit 100 exactly?

Exploring with Unifix® Cubes

1. Tell each group of children to show 14 with their cubes (1 ten-cube stick and 4 loose cubes).

2. Record the number 14 where everyone can see it. Use a large piece of paper, the chalkboard, or record it on the overhead projector.

3. Tell the children you are going to add sixes over and over. Tell the groups to add six cubes and make a ten-cube stick if they can. Ask them to tell you about the number now and record it (2 ten-cube sticks and no loose cubes).

4. Continue, having the groups add six cubes at a time and making ten-cube sticks if possible, then telling the number for you to record. Stop when you hit 100 or go over.

Recording the Connection

1. Tell the groups that they are going to repeat this activity, choosing their own starting number (between 10 and 20), and their own adding number (between 2 and 10). Have each group record these two numbers on the recording sheet.

2. Each group should work separately, adding cubes and recording the numbers. If time permits, the groups can try the activity several times with different starting numbers and different adding numbers.

Reporting and Displaying

Display the recording sheets where everyone can see them. Ask the children to tell you some things they notice about the lists of numbers. Talk about how they are alike and how they are different. Ask children to suggest ways they could put the recording sheets into groups.

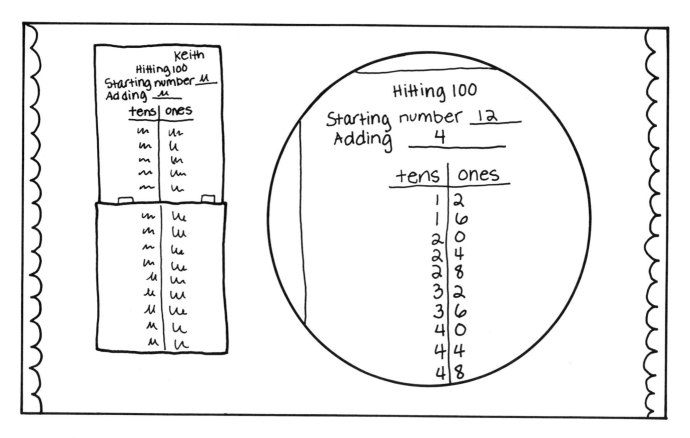

Solutions and Suggestions

It is interesting to look at the different number sequences several ways. Group them by the ending number (all those where 98 is the closest to 100, for example), or group them by the adding number (all those where the adding number is 6, for example). Children will notice many interesting patterns.

Another day, start at 100 (10 ten-cube sticks) and work backwards, taking away the same number each time and recording the number sequence. Look for sequences that end exactly at zero.

For more activity ideas, see *Understanding Place Value: Addition and Subtraction*, Creative Publications, Catalog Number 10965.

CONNECTIONS: GRADE 2
© 1989 Creative Publications

Hitting 100

Names _____

_____

Starting Number_____

Adding_____

tens	ones

paste

CONNECTIONS: GRADE 2
Hitting 100 Recording Sheet
© 1989 Creative Publications

Picturing Addition

In this lesson, children learn to apply regrouping skills to two-digit addition problems. They use cubes to represent problems and they link the addition algorithm to the way the cubes look. Use after children have had experience with regrouping and are starting to use the addition algorithm.

Classroom Organization

Eight groups of four sharing materials
Working together

Materials

Each group of four children will need these materials:
• 75 Unifix® Cubes • 8 copies of Picturing Addition Recording Sheet, page 47

CONNECTIONS: GRADE 2
© 1989 Creative Publications

Introducing the Problem

Today you are going to work together and use your cubes to make pictures of addition problems.

What do you think a picture of an addition problem looks like?

Exploring with Unifix® Cubes

1. Write this problem and its solution on the chalkboard. Challenge the children to work together in their groups and show the problem with cubes. Have them show a way to find the answer with those cubes.

$$\begin{array}{r} 36 \\ +\ 16 \\ \hline 52 \end{array}$$

2. When everyone has made an attempt, give different children an opportunity to describe what they did. They should have some version of 3 tens, 6 ones in one place and 1 ten, 6 ones in another place. After they move the cubes to add, they should have 5 tens and 2 ones. Have them tell what they did to get the answer.

3. Erase the answer and tell the children to watch as you solve the problem *the math way* writing down the 2, carrying the 1, and writing the 5. Have the children look at their cubes and *the math way* of finding the answer to the problem. Ask them why they think we write the numbers like this.

   - Can you see the 12 ones in the cubes? In the problem?
   - Can you see the 4 tens in the cubes? In the problem?
   - Can you see the regrouped ones (the new ten)? In the cubes? In the problem?
   - Why do you think we write *2* and put a *1* above the problem?

Recording the Connection

1. Have children work together to make up and solve their own addition problems with Unifix Cubes.

2. Show them how to record their work on the Picturing Addition Recording Sheet (page 47). Encourage them to do several different problems.

Reporting and Displaying

After the groups have each completed several different recording sheets, discuss a few of them together. It is important for children to have many opportunities to explain how the numbers in the problems relate to the way the cubes look. The goal is for children to be able to picture their addition problems with cubes and then explain how the numbers work.

Children may wish to put their recording sheets together into booklets. Unifix Cubes and extra recording sheets could also be set up as an independent math center where children could continue working on addition problems on another day.

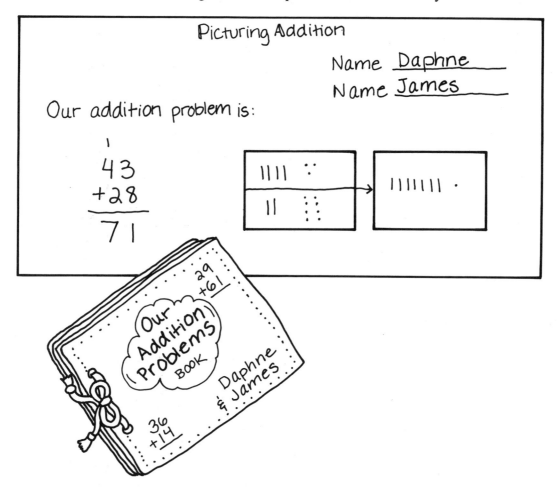

Suggestions

For more activity ideas, see *Understanding Place Value: Addition and Subtraction*, Creative Publications, Catalog Number 10965.

Picturing Addition   Names _____

_____

Our addition problem is:

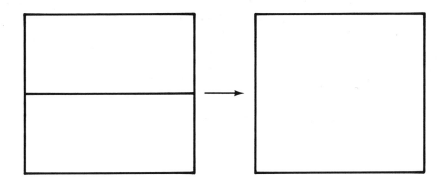

- -

Picturing Addition   Names _____

_____

Our addition problem is:

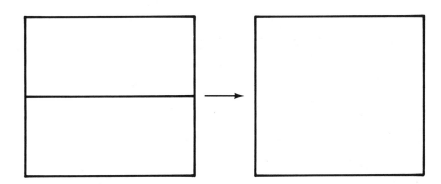

CONNECTIONS: GRADE 2
Picturing Addition Recording Sheet
© 1989 Creative Publications

Picturing Subtraction

In this lesson, children learn to apply regrouping skills to two-digit subtraction problems. They use cubes to represent problems and they link the subtraction algorithm to the way the cubes look. Use after children have had experience with regrouping and are starting to use the subtraction algorithm.

Classroom Organization

Eight groups of four sharing materials
Working together

Materials

Each group of four children will need these materials:
• 75 Unifix® Cubes • 8 copies of Picturing Subtraction Recording Sheet, page 51

Introducing the Problem

Today you are going to work together and use your cubes to make pictures of subtraction problems.

What do you think a picture of a subtraction problem looks like?

Exploring with Unifix® Cubes

1. Write this problem and its solution on the chalkboard. Challenge the children to work together in their groups and show the problem (before they subtract) with cubes. Then, have them show a way to find the answer with those cubes.

$$\begin{array}{r} 35 \\ -\ 17 \\ \hline 18 \end{array}$$

2. When everyone has made an attempt, give different children an opportunity to describe what they did. They should show some version of 3 tens and 5 ones. After they move the cubes to subtract, (changing tens into ones when necessary), they should have 1 ten and 8 ones. Have them tell what they did to get the answer.

3. Erase the answer and tell the children to watch as you solve the problem *the math way*. First regroup 3 tens and 5 ones into 2 tens and 15 ones. Then subtract 7 from 15 and write down the 8, next subtract 1 from 2 and write down the 1.

4. Have the children look at their cubes and this way of finding the answer to the problem. Ask them why they think we write the numbers like this.

   Can you show the 3 tens 5 ones regrouped to 2 tens 15 ones with your cubes? Where is it in the problem?

   What do the little *2* and the little *1* in the problem mean?

Recording the Connection

1. Have children work together to make up and solve their own subtraction problems with Unifix Cubes.

2. Show them how to record their work on the Picturing Subtraction Recording Sheet (page 51). Encourage them to do several different problems.

Reporting and Displaying

After the groups have completed several different recording sheets, discuss a few of them together. It is important for children to have many opportunities to explain how the numbers in the problems relate to the way the cubes look. The goal is for children to be able to picture their subtraction problems with cubes and then explain how the numbers work.

Children may wish to put together their recording sheets into booklets. Unifix Cubes and extra recording sheets could also be set up as an independent math center where children could continue working on subtraction problems on other days.

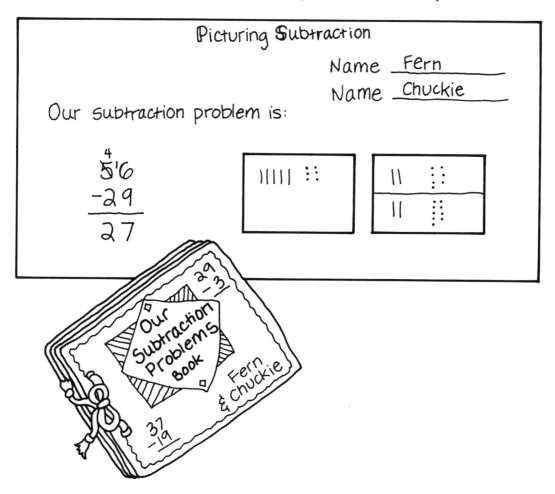

Suggestions

For more activity ideas, see *Understanding Place Value: Addition and Subtraction*, Creative Publications, Catalog Number 10965.

CONNECTIONS: GRADE 2
© 1989 Creative Publications

Picturing Subtraction

Names _____

_____

Our subtraction problem is:

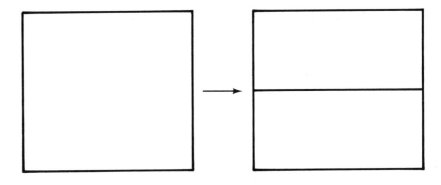

- -

Picturing Subtraction

Names _____

_____

Our subtraction problem is:

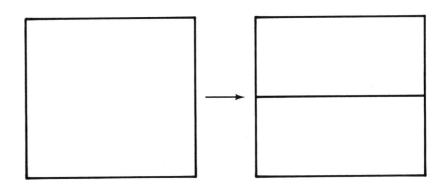

Kitty Bank Money Count

In this lesson, children count collections of money and write the total value. The manipulative helps children connect a concrete model to the abstract concept of skip counting. Use this lesson as reinforcement after teaching the children to count groups of coins.

Classroom Organization

Eight groups of four sharing materials
Working independently

Materials

Each group of four children will need these materials:
• 1 set of plastic coins • 8 copies of Kitty Bank Money Count Recording Sheet, page 55
• 4 sheets of Paper Coins, page 92 • Crayons, scissors, and paste

CONNECTIONS: GRADE 2
© 1989 Creative Publications

Introducing the Problem

You are going to put coins in your kitty bank and then count to see how much money you have.

Can you make banks with two different amounts of money?

Exploring with Plastic Coins

1. Tell the children they should take enough coins to cover the bank.

2. Have them take turns counting their money collection aloud, saying the total amount.

Recording the Connection

1. Tell the children to make a different collection with coins. They should count the collection, write the skip-counting numbers, and the total amount.

2. Tell them to paste paper coins onto the bank to match their collection.

3. Continue with several banks, making different collections.

Reporting and Displaying

When many banks are completed, tell the children that you want to display them on the wall. Arrange the banks where everyone can see them and say, **How can we put these banks into groups that are alike in some way?**

Children may suggest grouping the banks based on the number of coins each bank contains (all the banks with 12 coins, for example) or grouping the banks based on total amounts of money (all the banks that have 74 cents, for example). It would also be interesting to group the banks in order from least to greatest amount of money.

Choose one of the ways children suggest. Sort the banks and display them on a bulletin board.

Solutions and Suggestions

There are many ways to sort the banks. On successive days, children may wish to reclassify the banks based on other criteria. Give children many opportunities to discuss the likenesses and differences among the banks.

CONNECTIONS: GRADE 2
© 1989 Creative Publications

Kitty Bank Money Count

Name _____

_____

_____

Total Amount _____

Make A Name for Yourself

In this lesson, children use an alphabet list that assigns coins to letters to find the value of different words, including their names. Using the list, they take a group of plastic coins to match the name and record the value. Use this lesson to practice counting collections of coins.

Classroom Organization

Eight groups of four sharing materials
 Working independently

Materials

Each group of four children will need these materials:
• 1 set of plastic coins • 4 copies of Make a Name for Yourself Recording Sheet, page 59 • 4 sheets of Paper Coins, page 92 • Scissors and paste

Introducing the Problem

What if you had to buy the letters in your name? Let's find out how much your name would cost.

What is the price of your name?

Exploring with Plastic Coins

1. Have the children look at their recording sheets. Explain that each letter is worth a certain amount of money. For example, an A costs 1 cent, a B costs 5 cents, and so on.

2. Have the children suggest a word, then work together to find out how much it costs (*brontosaurus*, for example).

   b = 5 cents
   r = 5 cents
   o = 10 cents
   n = 5 cents
   t = 25 cents
   o = 10 cents
   s = 10 cents
   a = 1 cent
   u = 1 cent
   r = 5 cents
   u = 1 cent
   s = 10 cents

   The word *brontosaurus* costs 88 cents!

3. Tell the children to find out how much their names cost. Have them take coins to match the letters in their names. Select a few examples and discuss them with the class.

Recording the Connection

1. Have the children complete their recording sheets by writing their names and pasting the appropriate paper coins next to each letter.

2. Next, they should count the coins and write the amounts next to their names.

Reporting and Displaying

When the name strips are complete, discuss different ways to display them on the wall. They could be sorted and classified by like amounts. They could be put in order from least to greatest amount. They could be arranged by numbers of coins. Choose one of the ways children suggest and work together to display the name strips on the board.

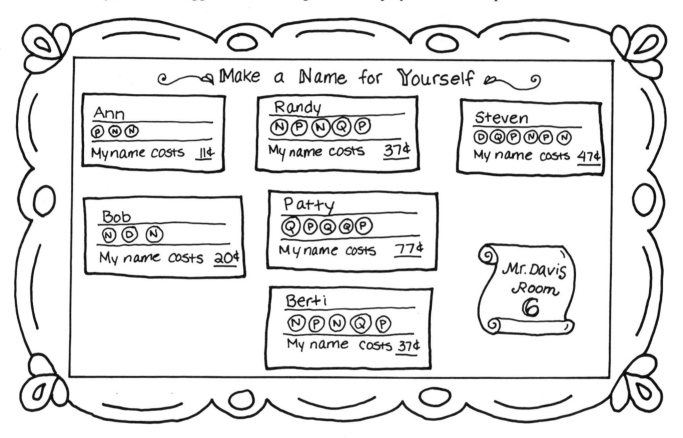

Solutions and Suggestions

Since there are several ways to sort the strips, it will be interesting for the children to display them one way for a day or so and then rearrange the strips another way for a different display. This will give children an opportunity to discuss and compare different ways of thinking about the coins.

Pick other interesting words and find out what they cost (*dinosaur*, *skateboard*, *hamburger*, *television*, for example).

CONNECTIONS: GRADE 2
© 1989 Creative Publications

Make a Name for Yourself

A	B	C	D	E	F	G	H	I

J	K	L	M	N	O	P	Q	R

S	T	U	V	W	X	Y	Z

My name costs _____

CONNECTIONS: GRADE 2
Make a Name for Yourself Recording Sheet
© 1989 Creative Publications

Two Hands Full

In this lesson, children learn to show an amount of money in two ways with two different collections of coins. Children practice counting money collections then recording by writing the skip-counting numbers. Use this lesson to practice counting money.

Classroom Organization

Eight groups of four sharing materials
Working independently

Materials

Each group of four children will need these materials:
• 1 set of plastic coins • 8 copies of Two Hands Full Recording Sheet, page 63
• 4 sheets of Paper Coins, page 92 • Scissors and paste

CONNECTIONS: GRADE 2
© 1989 Creative Publications

Introducing the Problem

Let's say you went to the store and paid 41 cents for a toy. We are going to find out what coins you might use to make that 41 cents.

Do you think there is more than one way?

Exploring with Plastic Coins

1. Tell the children to put out these coins: dime, dime, dime, dime, penny.

2. Practice counting this collection of coins aloud: **10, 20, 30, 40, 41**.

3. Tell the children to put out these coins: quarter, dime, nickel, penny.

4. Count this collection aloud: **25, 35, 40, 41**.

5. Discuss that the two collections have the same value even though the coins are different.

6. Start with a different amount of money, asking children to find two ways to make that amount.

Recording the Connection

1. Children should put their own collections of money on one of the hands of the recording sheet.

2. They should count their collections and record by writing the skip-counting numbers. They should paste paper coins onto the hand to match.

3. Tell the children to find another way to make the same amount of money with different coins. Record by pasting paper coins on the empty hand of the recording sheet and writing the skip-counting numbers.

Reporting and Displaying

When each child has had a chance to complete two recording sheets, collect the pages and arrange them for everyone to see. Organize the recording sheets on a wall, grouping those with like amounts together. Let children take turns counting different collections aloud, saying the skip-counting numbers.

Ask children to tell you why they think it is that two different groups of coins can be worth the same amount.

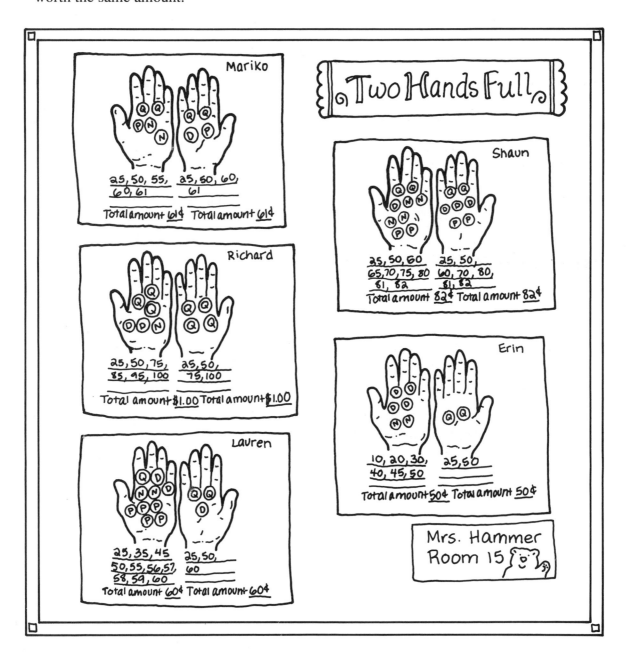

CONNECTIONS: GRADE 2
© 1989 Creative Publications

Two Hands Full

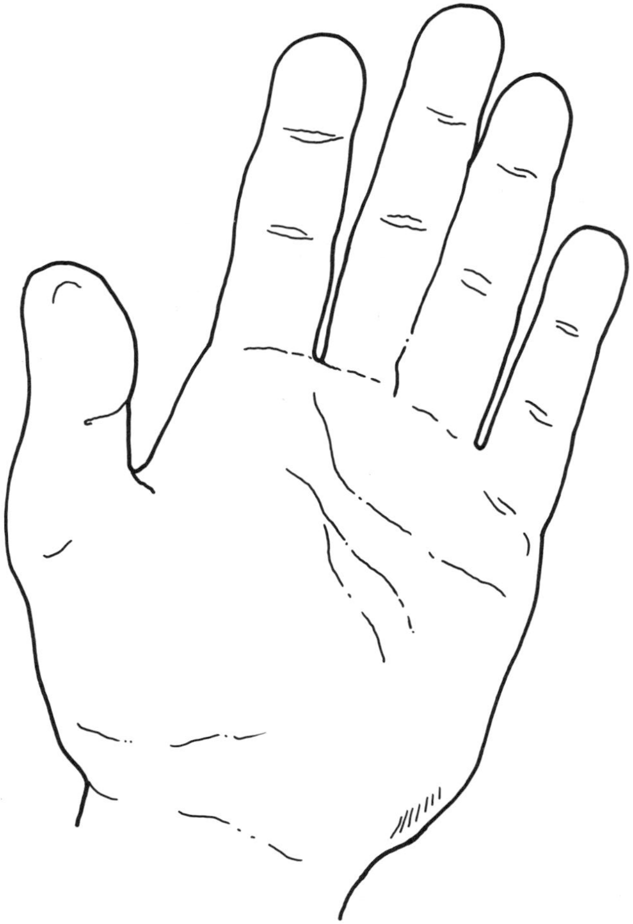

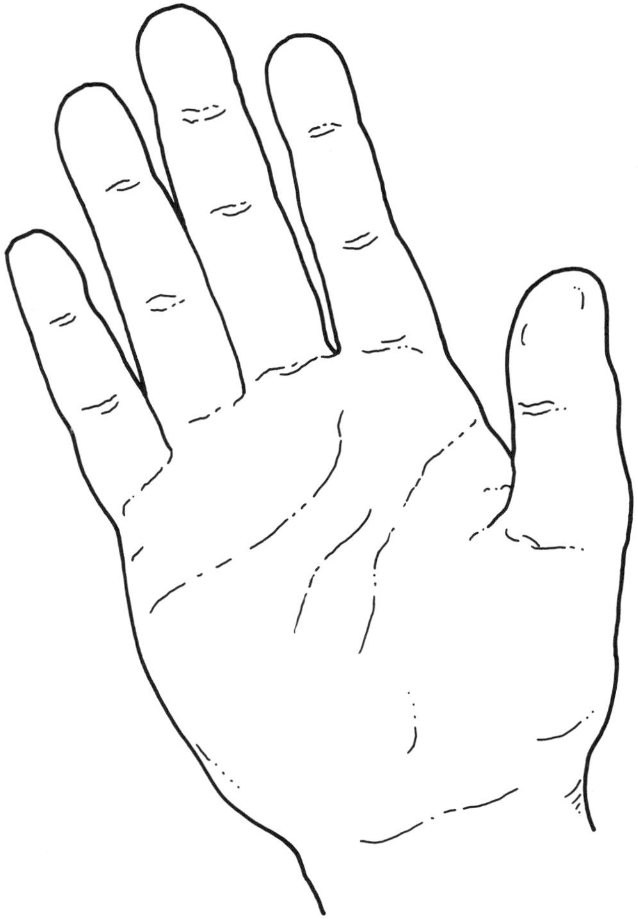

Total amount _____

Total amount _____

CONNECTIONS: GRADE 2
Two Hands Full Recording Sheet

63

A Dollar Here, A Dollar There

In this lesson, children use plastic money to find different collections that have a value of one dollar. Use this lesson to practice counting different groups of coins.

Classroom Organization

Eight groups of four sharing materials
Working independently

Materials

Each group of four will need these materials:
• 1 set of plastic coins • 8 sheets of Paper Coins, page 92 • 8 copies of A Dollar Here, A Dollar There Recording Sheet, page 67 • Scissors and paste

Introducing the Problem

Let's see if we can find different ways to make a dollar with these coins: quarters, dimes, nickels, and pennies.

Do you think you can find two different ways?

Exploring with Plastic Coins

1. Review the values of the different coins: penny, nickel, dime, quarter.

2. Tell the children that they are trying to find different ways to make a dollar with coins. They should arrange coins on the dollar bill outline on the recording sheet.

3. Discuss and compare the different ways children make a dollar. Have them describe their collections and count the coins aloud.

Recording the Connection

1. To record their work, children should paste paper coins inside the dollar outline on their recording sheets.

2. The children should complete their recording sheets to show the number of each type of coin used.

Reporting and Displaying

When each child has completed several recording sheets, display the sheets so everyone can see them. Discuss ways the collections are alike and different. Work together to plan different ways to organize the dollar collections. You might put them in order from least number of coins to greatest, or you might sort them according to a common characteristic.

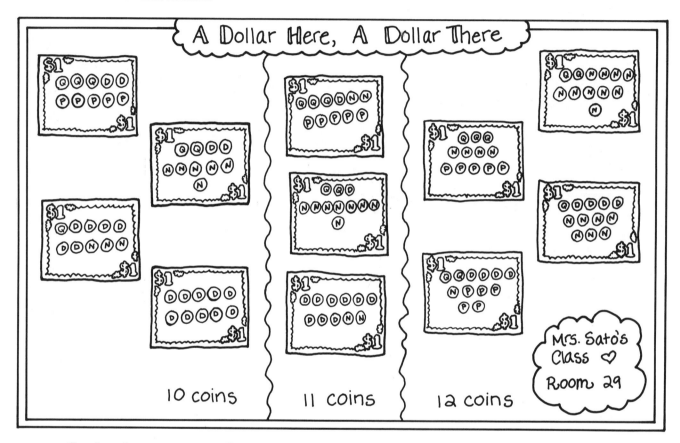

Solutions and Suggestions

There are 242 ways to use coins to make a dollar, using only quarters, dimes, nickels, and pennies. There is one way with 4 quarters, 12 ways with 3 quarters, 36 ways with 2 quarters, 72 ways with 1 quarter, and 121 ways with zero quarters. The ways with 3 quarters are listed below. You are not asking your children to find all the ways, but to organize the ways they do find into interesting groups.

QQQ DD N
QQQ DD PPPPP
QQQ D NNN
QQQ D NN PPPPP
QQQ D N PPPPP PPPPP
QQQ D PPPPP PPPPP PPPPP

QQQ NNNNN
QQQ NNNN PPPPP
QQQ NNN PPPPP PPPPP
QQQ NN PPPPP PPPPP PPPPP
QQQ N PPPPP PPPPP PPPPP PPPPP
QQQ PPPPP PPPPP PPPPP PPPPP PPPPP

A Dollar Here, A Dollar There

Name _____

Q	D	N	P	Total number of coins

CONNECTIONS: GRADE 2
A Dollar Here, A Dollar There Recording Sheet
© 1989 Creative Publications

Tiny Turtle Parade

In this lesson, children use Pattern Blocks to cover a turtle outline. They exchange blocks for other blocks to find different ways to cover the same space. Use this lesson to enhance visual thinking, spatial skills, and problem-solving abilities.

Classroom Organization

Eight groups of four sharing materials
Working together

Materials

Each group of four children will need these materials:
• Pattern Blocks, see page 3 • 4 copies of Tiny Turtle Parade Recording Sheet, page 71
• Crayons

CONNECTIONS: GRADE 2
© 1989 Creative Publications

Introducing the Problem

The tiny turtles are going out to march in the parade. They always march in order with the turtles covered with the least number of blocks at the front of the line.

How many different turtles do you think will march in the parade?

Exploring with Pattern Blocks

1. Tell the children to cover the turtles on their recording sheets with blocks. Note that there is a triangle grid inside the turtle to help the children when they color to record. Blocks other than triangles will fit on the grid, and children should be encouraged to use them to cover the turtle.

2. Have children count the number of blocks they used.

3. Explain to the groups that their task is to find four different ways to cover the turtle with blocks.

Recording the Connection

1. When the groups have found four different ways to cover the turtle, they should record each way by coloring the grids to show the blocks.

2. Below the turtles, they should write the number of blocks used in each solution.

Reporting and Displaying

When each group has four turtles covered with different numbers of blocks, work together as a class to make the parade. Find the turtles covered with the least number of blocks, the next greater, and so on to the turtles covered with the greatest number of blocks.

Some groups may want to use extra recording sheets to find ways with other numbers of blocks.

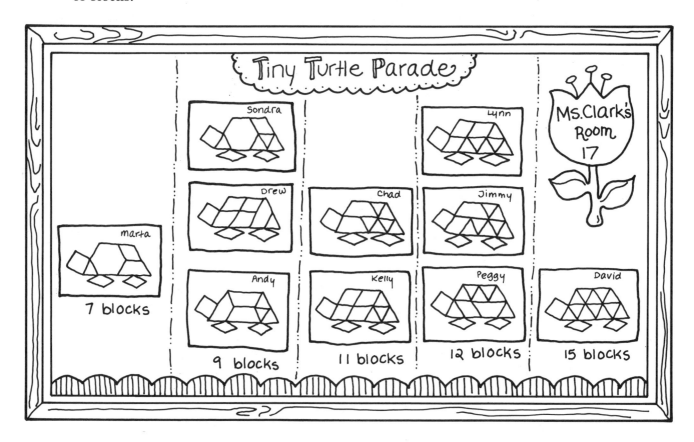

Solutions and Suggestions

The least number of blocks needed to cover Tiny Turtle is 7. The greatest number of blocks needed is 15. It is possible to cover Tiny Turtle with every number of blocks in between.

For more activity ideas, see *Hands On Pattern Blocks*, Creative Publications, Catalog Number 34489.

CONNECTIONS: GRADE 2
© 1989 Creative Publications

Tiny Turtle Parade

Name _____

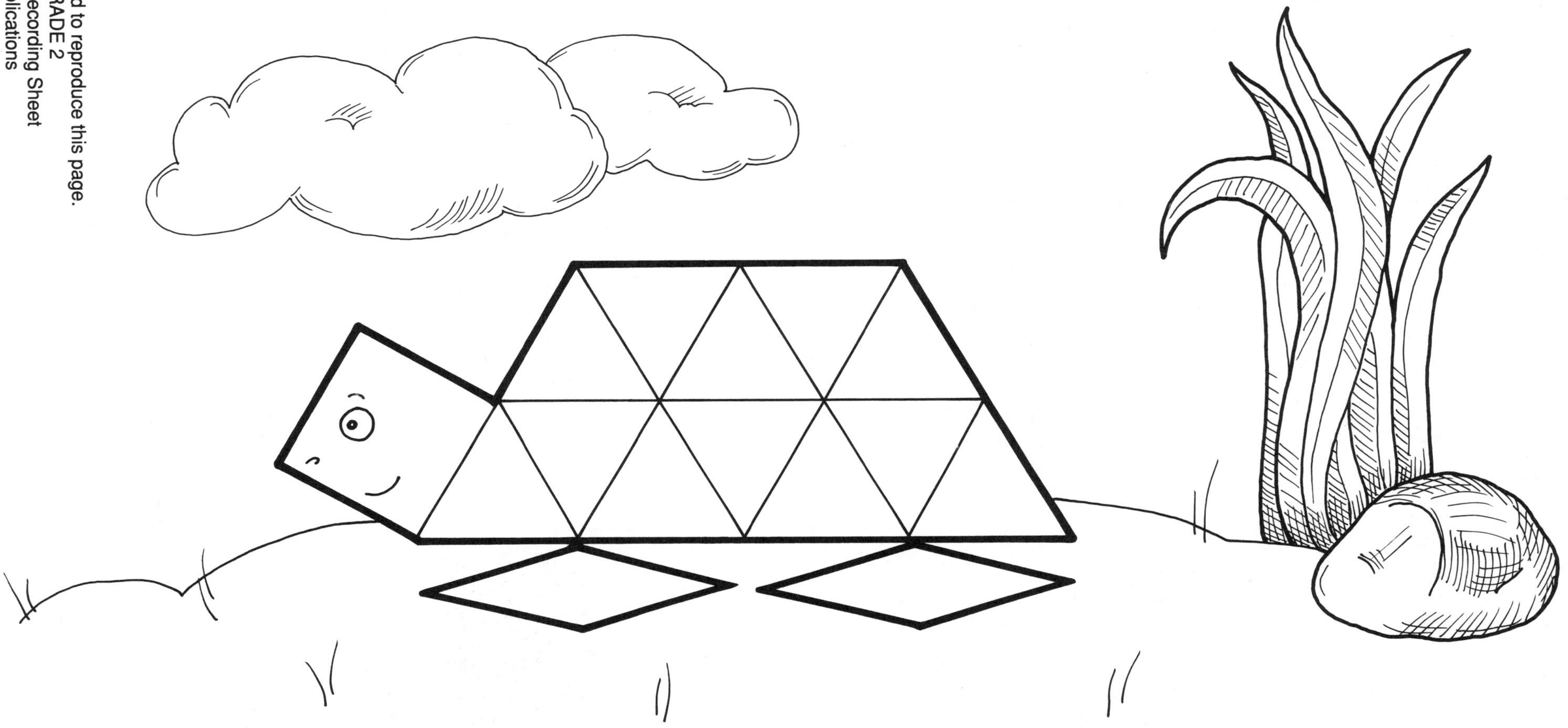

Number of blocks _____

CONNECTIONS: GRADE 2
Tiny Turtle Parade Recording Sheet
© 1989 Creative Publications

71

Triangle Tessellations

In this lesson, children search for different ways to cover a traingle with Pattern Blocks. They choose one way and make many copies of it, then use these triangles to make a tessellation. This lesson builds spatial thinking, geometric concepts, and problem-solving abilities.

Classroom Organization

Eight groups of four sharing materials
Working together

Materials

Each group of four will need these materials:
• Patterns Blocks, see page 3 • 4 copies of Triangle Tessellations Recording Sheet, page 75 • 1 large sheet of butcher paper • Scissors, crayons, and paste

CONNECTIONS: GRADE 2
© 1989 Creative Publications

Introducing the Problem

Each of your groups is going to make a banner with tessellating triangles. Triangles tessellate because they fit together with no spaces.

What do you think the banner your group makes will look like?

Exploring with Pattern Blocks

1. Tell the children to take three blue blocks and three green blocks.

2. Tell them to use the blocks to cover one of the triangles on their recording sheets. (There is a triangle grid inside the triangles to help the children when they color to record. Blocks other than green triangles will fit on the grid and should also be used to cover the triangle.)

3. They should try different ways and decide as a group which one arrangement they will choose for their group banner.

Recording the Connection

1. Each child should color a triangle grid to match the blocks in the arrangement that the group selected.

2. Each child should color eight more triangles like the first one so the group has a total of 36 triangles. They should cut out the triangles.

3. Have them arrange their 36 triangles into a tessellation. Encourage them to try several different arrangements.

4. When the groups have chosen their favorite tessellation patterns, have them paste their triangles in position on the butcher paper to make their banners.

Reporting and Displaying

After all the groups have made their banners, let the children talk about how they chose their way of putting the triangles together. Talk about how the banners are alike and how they are different.

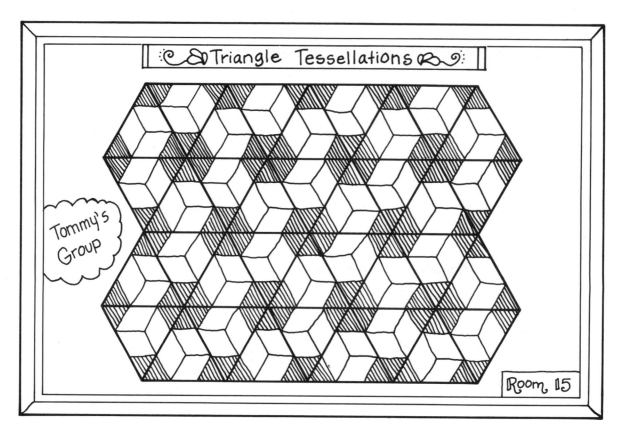

Solutions and Suggestions

Here are five ways that have been found to cover the triangle. Children will find many ways to arrange each of these into tessellation patterns.

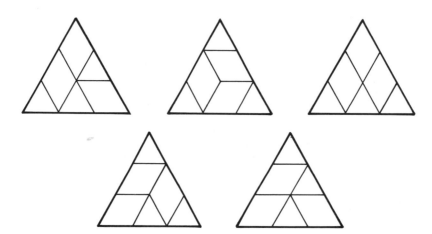

CONNECTIONS: GRADE 2
© 1989 Creative Publications

Triangle Tessellations

CONNECTIONS: GRADE 2
Triangle Tesselations Recording Sheet
© 1989 Creative Publications

Cinnamon Crackers

In this lesson, children trace shapes made with Pattern Blocks and shade fractional parts of each shape. They write the fraction numerals to match the shaded parts. Use this lesson as an extension and reinforcement after you have taught the concepts of fractional parts.

Classroom Organization

Eight groups of four sharing materials
Working together

Materials

Each group of four children will need these materials:
• Pattern Blocks, see page 3 • 12 copies of the Cinnamon Crackers Recording Sheet, page 79 • Brown crayons

CONNECTIONS: GRADE 2
© 1989 Creative Publications

Introducing the Problem

Today we are going to make shapes for crackers out of Pattern Blocks. When the crackers are made, we are going to sprinkle cinnamon on a fractional part of them.

What are some different fractions that you might be able to show?

Exploring with Pattern Blocks

1. Tell the children to make shapes with two blocks just alike. Talk about what one-half of the shape would be (one of the blocks). Have the groups make many examples.

2. Tell the children to make shapes with three blocks just alike. Talk about what one-third of the shape would be (one of the blocks). Talk about what two-thirds of the shape would be (two of the blocks). Have the groups make many examples.

3. Tell the children to make shapes with four blocks just alike. Talk about what one-fourth, two-fourths, and three-fourths of the shape would be. Have the children make many examples.

Recording the Connection

1. Have children make a cracker shape with two blocks just alike and trace it onto the recording sheet.

2. Children should *sprinkle cinnamon* onto one-half of the cracker by shading with a brown crayon. Children should write the fraction on the recording sheet.

3. Children should continue making different crackers with two blocks and shading one-half, then switch to three blocks, and four blocks. They should shade to show one-third, two-thirds, one-fourth, two-fourths, three-fourths.

Reporting and Displaying

When each child has made several different cinnamon cracker pictures, collect them and display them on a wall. Have the children help you organize the pictures into groups, putting crackers together that are alike in some way. Organize them one way one day and discuss the things that children notice, then let the children change the organization another day and discuss again.

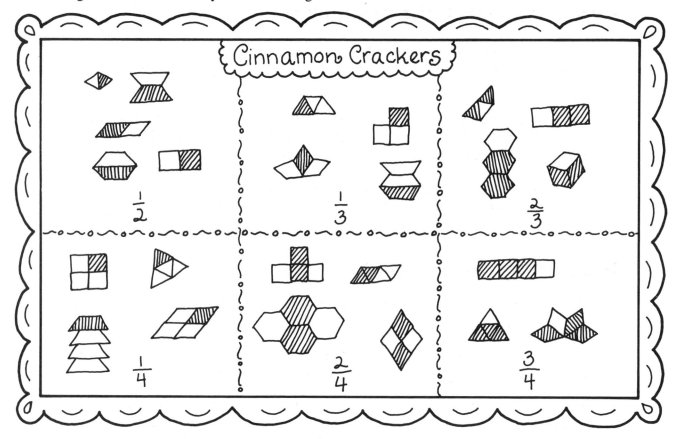

Solutions and Suggestions

There are many different crackers that can be made with Pattern Blocks and many different ways they can be shaded to show fractional parts. One way to organize them is by the fraction they show, another by the color of blocks, another by the number of parts shaded.

Cinnamon Crackers

Name _____

_____ of the cracker has cinnamon.

- -

Cinnamon Crackers

Name _____

_____ of the cracker has cinnamon.

Bears in Boat Races

In this lesson, children use Teddy Bear Counters to learn the concept of multiplication. Children arrange equal groups of bears in boats and write the multiplication equation that describes their picture. Use this lesson either to introduce or reinforce multiplication concepts.

Classroom Organization

Eight groups of four sharing materials
Working independently

Materials

Each group of four children will need these materials:
• 37 Teddy Bear Counters • 5 copies of Paper Teddy Bears, page 91 • 8 copies of Bears in Boat Races Recording Sheets, page 83 • 8 sheets of construction paper • Crayons, scissors, paste

CONNECTIONS: GRADE 2
© 1989 Creative Publications

Introducing the Problem

The bears are having boat races today! The rules say that for each race the same number of bears must be in each boat. We are going to write multiplication equations to tell about the races.

What do you think the first race will look like?

Exploring with Teddy Bear Counters

1. Tell the children to put out three boats for the first race. Tell them to put four teddy bears on each boat. Model the language, **Three boats with four bears in each boat, 12 bears altogether**.

2. Have several children practice the language you have just modeled. Say, **This is the math way to tell this story—three times four equals twelve**. Practice the math way.

3. Tell the children to make up different boat race pictures with different numbers of boats and bears. Just remember the rule: each boat in a race must have the same number of bears.

4. Take turns letting the children tell about their boat race pictures, using the story language and the math language of the equation.

Recording the Connection

1. Tell the children to make a boat race picture to paste down. They should paste several boats on a piece of paper and put teddy bears on them.

2. Next, they should write the multiplication equation that tells about the picture.

3. Then the children should paste paper bears on the boats to finish their picture.

4. Let the children make as many different Bears in Boat Races pictures as they can.

Reporting and Displaying

Put up a large lake bulletin board and arrange the pictures that the children make. Ask the children to suggest ways to arrange the pictures.

Solutions and Suggestions

If you organize the pictures in a large matrix, you can show the multiplication table or the *easy facts* part of it. Children can make more boat race pictures to fill in missing equations.

For more activity ideas, see *Understanding Operations: Multiplication and Division*, Creative Publications, Catalog Number 31052.

Bears in Boat Races

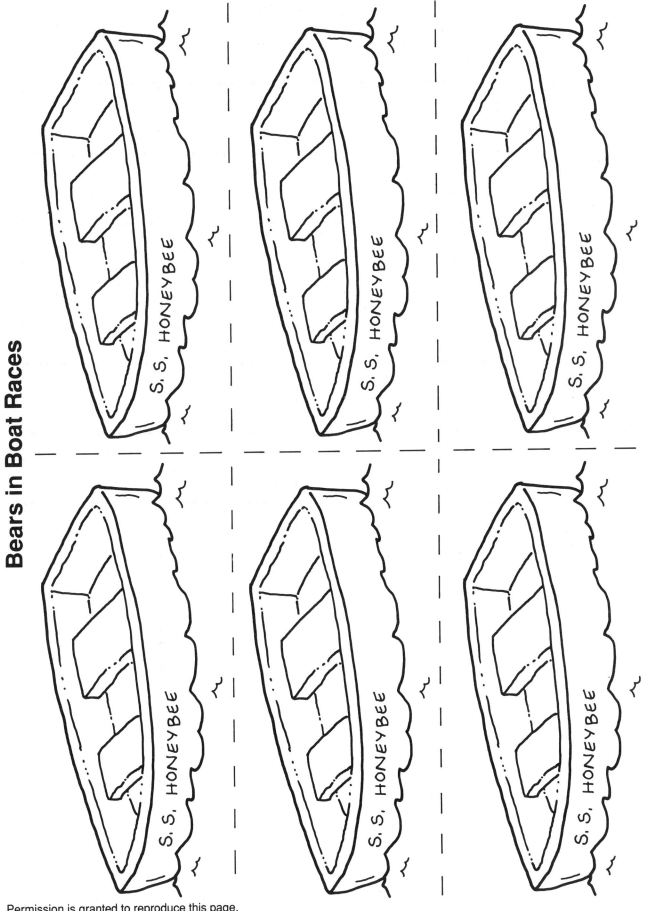

CONNECTIONS: GRADE 2
Bears in Boat Races Recording Sheet
© 1989 Creative Publications

Unifix® Paper

See page 3 for directions.

Centimeter Grid Paper

See page 3 for directions.

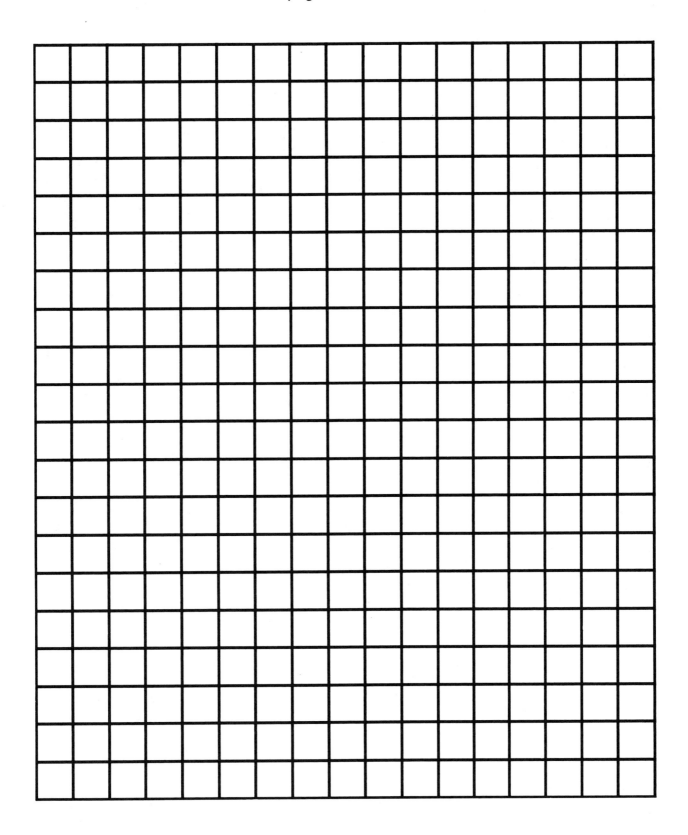

CONNECTIONS: GRADE 2
Centimeter Grid Paper

Paper Pattern Blocks

See page 3 for directions.

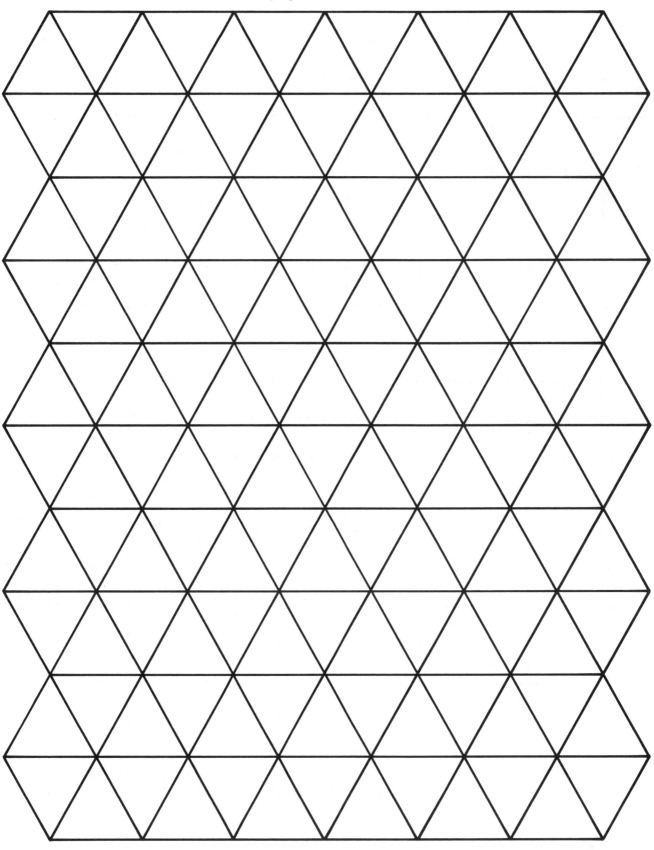

Paper Pattern Blocks

See page 3 for directions.

CONNECTIONS: GRADE 2
Paper Pattern Blocks

87

Paper Pattern Blocks

See page 3 for directions.

Paper Pattern Blocks

See page 3 for directions.

CONNECTIONS: GRADE 2
Paper Pattern Blocks

Paper Pattern Blocks

See page 3 for directions.

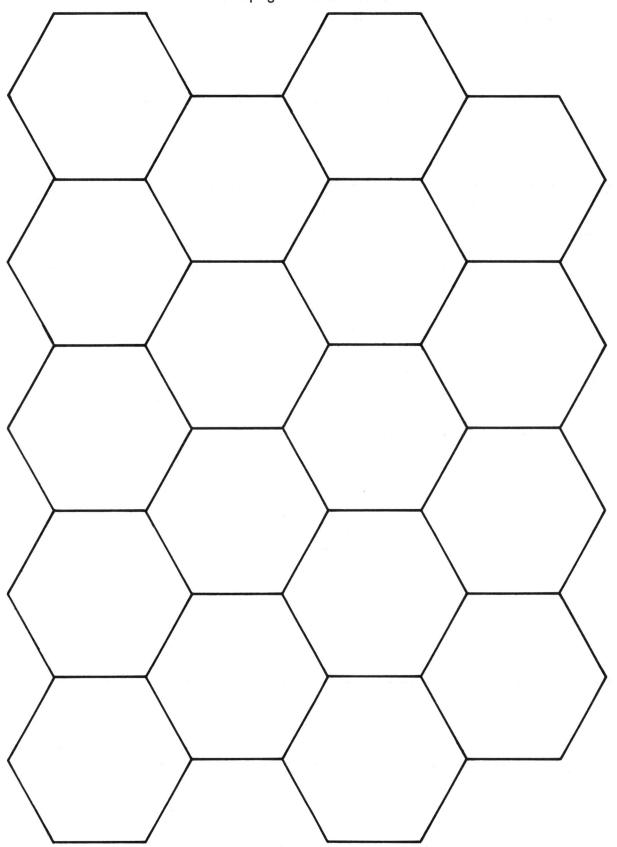

CONNECTIONS: GRADE 2
Paper Pattern Blocks
© 1989 Creative Publications

Paper Teddy Bears

See page 3 for directions.

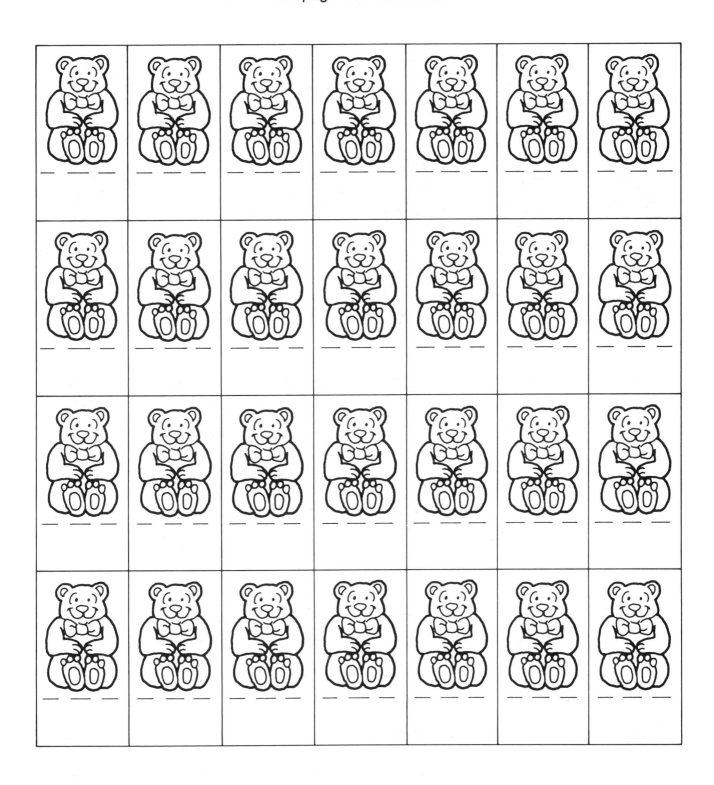

CONNECTIONS: GRADE 2
Centimeter Grid Paper

Paper Coins

See page 3 for directions.

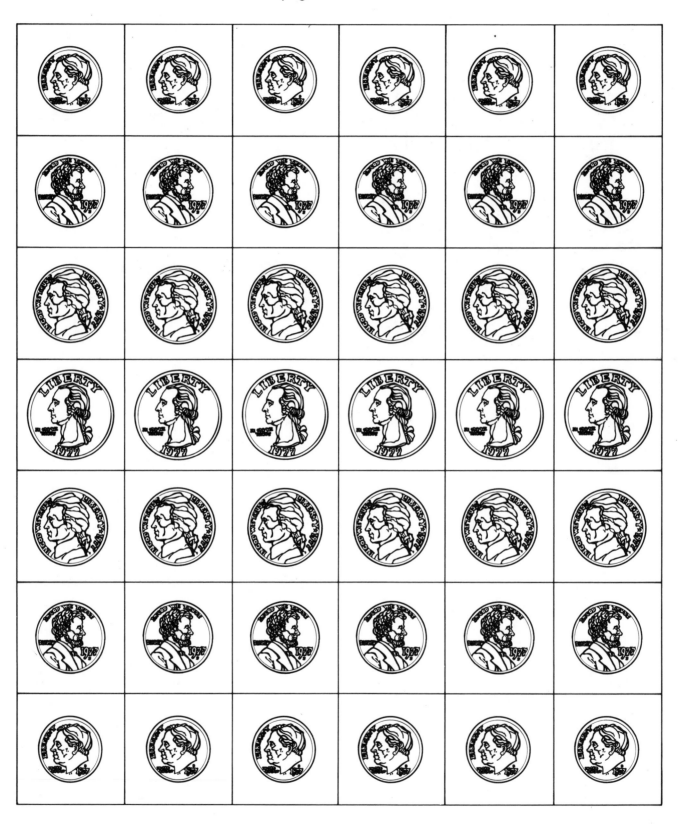

CONNECTIONS: GRADE 2
Centimeter Grid Paper
© 1989 Creative Publications